Working with Indigenous Elders

Jonathan H. Ellerby

An Introductory Handbook Based on the Teachings of Winnipeg-Area Indigenous Elders and Cultural Teachers

NATIONAL LIBRARY OF CANADA
CATALOGUING IN PUBLICATION DATA

Working with Indigenous Elders: an introductory handbook for institution-based and health care professionals based on the teachings of Winnipeg-area indigenous elders and cultural teachers / Jonathan H. Ellerby.

Includes bibliographic references.

3rd ed.

ISBN 0-13-197843-8

1. Transcultural medical care--Manitoba--Winnipeg. 2. Native peoples--Medical care--Manitoba--Winnipeg. 3. Native peoples--Health and hygiene--Manitoba--Winnipeg. 4. Elders (Native peoples)--Manitoba.
I. Ellerby, Jonathan H. Working with Aboriginal elders. II. Title.

E78.M25E44 2006   362.1'089'970712743   C2005-903296-0

Other Publications
available from Aboriginal Issues Press
(formerly Native Studies Press):

Aboriginal Health, Identity and Resources

Pushing the Margins: Native and Northern Studies

Native Voices in Research

Aboriginal Cultural Landscapes

Seeing the World with Aboriginal Eyes

Gambling and Problem Gambling in First Nations Communities

Working with Indigenous Elders

Previously published as Working with Aboriginal Elders.
An introductory handbook based on the teachings of Winnipeg area Indigenous Elders and cultural teachers, prepared by Jonathan H. Ellerby.

Information published in this book is the sole opinions of the author and not those of the University of Manitoba or the Aboriginal Issues Press, its employees, editors, and volunteers. All profits from the sale of this book are used to support the refereed publication of Indigenous scholarship through the Aboriginal Issues Press Endowment Fund at the University of Manitoba.

1st Edition, Published by Earth Concepts, Printed by Biomedical Communications, Winnipeg, Canada

2nd Edition, Published by Native Studies Press, Printed in Canada by Hignell Book Printing, Cover design and layout adapted from Jonathan Ellerby by Karen Armstrong Design, Edited by Jill Oakes and Rick Riewe.

3rd Edition, Published by Aboriginal Issues Press, Printed in Canada by Premier Printing, Cover design and layout by Karen Armstrong Design. Edited by Jill Oakes and Rick Riewe.

Additional Copies are available from:

Aboriginal Issues Press
Clayton H. Riddell
Faculty of Environment, Earth, and Resources
University of Manitoba
Winnipeg, Manitoba, R3T 2N2

Phone 1-204-474-7352
Fax   1-204-474-7699

E-Mail & Web   aboriginal_issues_press@umanitoba.ca

umanitoba.ca/environment/aboriginal_issues_press

iv

TABLE OF CONTENTS

vi

ACKNOWLEDGEMENTS

This unique and valuable project was made possible with the generous support, input, and selfless contributions of a number of people. While some have chosen to remain nameless, I acknowledge and thank Diane Morrisseau, Barbara Shoomski, Stan McKay, Art Shofley, Kathy Bird, and Kathrine Morrisseau-Sinclair. I also thank Gerry Berthelette, Joe Kaufert, Guy Lavallee, Laura Steiman Shofley, and Chris Trott for their support. Great thanks to David Gregory for his academic direction, support and openness - without him this would not have been possible.

I thank Gene Thin Elk and all the many Elders, traditional healers and spiritual leaders that I have been blessed to meet and learn from over the years. I hope that this project may honour and reflect some of the tremendous wisdom they have shared with me.

Finally, to those visionaries, Indigenous and non-Indigenous, who strive creatively and tirelessly to improve the quality of health and health care for Indigenous people through the appreciation and integration of culture: my deepest respect goes out to them - it has not been an easy road.

To all of my relations, Thank you.

Meegwetch.

Jonathan Ellerby

Part I.

Introduction:

Working with Indigenous Elders

BACKGROUND

Indigenous health care needs continue to grow in the Province of Manitoba and elsewhere in Canada and the United States. In response, health care facilities, like the Health Sciences Center, Winnipeg, and health care institutions like the Medical Services Branch, are striving for more effective approaches to treatment for Indigenous people and more responsible to the role that culture plays in the care of Indigenous people.

There are many models of culturally relevant care, from the community-based independent work of traditional healers, to the inclusion of Indigenous Elders in the institutional team care of Indigenous patients. Similarly, Elders and traditional healers have become involved in correctional programs, universities and community treatment programs of all types wherever Indigenous populations are in high numbers.

In order to improve, continue, and support collaborative care with Indigenous Elders, cross-cultural education is essential. As Indigenous specific needs are increasingly addressed, Elders must be involved as authorities on Indigenous culture and health. Successful relationships between Elders and institutional staff are crucial to the future of Indigenous care.

Administrative and treatment based relationships between Elders, traditional healers, cultural liaisons and non-Indigenous staff have often presented challenges largely attributed to a lack of inter-cultural understanding. The clarification of the traditional Elders' roles, practices, and philosophies of work and healing are necessary first steps in ensuring effective cooperation of Elders in institutions.

METHODOLOGY

This project was made possible through the generous cooperation of a number of Elders and Cultural Teachers who recognize the need to improve the relationship between Elders and institutions. The idea for this manual was developed from meetings with Winnipeg-area Elders and cultural advisors involved with health care agencies. Once the need for an educational manual was established, formal recorded, and informal non-recorded, interviews with Indigenous Elders and Indigenous cultural advisors, also referred to as teachers, took place. The cultural advisors were identified by a small group of Elders who made recommendations and attested to the quality of the individuals suggested for interviews.

Once the Elders' recommendations were made, the various Elders and cultural teachers were contacted. Cultural protocol was observed as much as possible and the original Elder committee assisted in approaching the interview candidates. All but one of the Elders and cultural teachers approached were willing to participate in this project. Private interviews were set at times and locations of convenience for the Elders and cultural advisors. This manual is based on the recorded interviews and private discussions provided by these Elders and advisors. Though there is a large body of literature written about Indigenous world view and tradition (see bibliography), this manual attempts to serve as a vehicle for sharing the living voices of Indigenous people.

The quoted and inset material was transcribed from original interviews and discussions. A copy of the draft of this manual was sent to each of the participating Elders and advisors for final review, corrections and approval. A great effort was made to respect the distinct views of each of the Indigenous Elders and Cultural Teachers involved in this project.

ADDITIONAL NOTES

The teachings that the Elders and cultural teachers shared in this manual come from a deep personal commitment to a healing role that is more a way of life than a definable job. What is presented is not a final statement on who Elders and healers are or what they do. To truly understand the life ways and teachings of traditional Indigenous Elders is a commitment that takes a lifetime. Rather, what is presented is merely one possible contribution towards better cross-cultural understanding.

It is critical to acknowledge that the teachings given here reflect the particular views of individual Elders and cultural teachers. Indigenous communities are extremely diverse in culture and practice. For example, within Manitoba alone there are Annishinaabe (Ojibway), Cree, Métis, Dene, Dakota (Sioux), Inuit, and other Indigenous communities and individuals - each maintaining distinct cultural beliefs and practices. Within each of these large groups there are variations in culture and language.

Furthermore, within even a single community there can be a wide range of individual beliefs and practices. The influence of Christian traditions is common in many places. In some cases, the presence of Christianity has replaced Indigenous tradition, in other cases they co-exist. There are few, if any, accurate cultural or psychosocial generalizations that can be made about all Indigenous people. Variation must be expected and treated with respect.

PART II.

BASIC UNDERSTANDING:

ROLES AND WORLDVIEWS OF ELDERS

ROLES AND WORLDVIEWS OF ELDERS

In nine years of experience working with and observing the work of Indigenous Elders and healers in institutional settings (universities, hospitals, and correctional facilities) it has become clear that the most common source of cross-cultural conflicts is a general lack of cultural education on the part of non-Indigenous professionals. This is not to suggest that sincere efforts have not been made; rather, this realization points to the factors that have complicated otherwise well-meaning program attempts.

Indigenous and Western institutional approaches to work and treatment of virtually all types appear irreconcilably incompatible. Yet experience in both successful and problematic cross-cultural environments shows that the argument that Indigenous approaches to treatment are invalid and incompatible with Western-based approaches is generally a perspective that is symptomatic of other types of conflict. Personality conflicts, individual biases, cultural ignorance, Western ethnocentrism, and the perception that Western paradigms are both flawless and superior to all others, are factors that have led to the artificial magnification of cultural difference. Successful programs, and institutions where conflict areas have been resolved, consistently show that the overall lack of understanding of the role and world view of Indigenous Elders is the origin of most cooperative breakdowns.

Many non-Indigenous professionals have the best interest of their patients or clients in mind when they react with great caution and skepticism to the clinical approaches of Elders that appear to differ vastly from their own. Further, many non-Indigenous professionals have little capacity to gauge the relative ability of an Elder. This discrepancy in understanding has ramifications for Indigenous people that reach beyond the management of individual patients. Socio-political power relationships are epitomized and maintained through the cultural dominance of Western medical practitioners over Indigenous Elders.

By becoming familiar with the basic beliefs of Elders and healers most professionals are relieved of their tendency towards suspicion and mistrust and may cooperatively pursue their common goal: the delivery of   effective care. The support of Indigenous approaches to health has the added effect of socially affirming Indigenous culture.

WHO IS AN ELDER?

There are a number of common themes that arise when Elders and cultural teachers are asked to describe who or what an Elder is. The first important point made is that the term "Elder" is often misused. An Elder is not anyone who says they are one, and an Elder is not just any older Indigenous person.

> *An Elder is not just somebody who just gets old.... It's usually somebody who is an example. They usually are people who have overcome a lot in their lives... It's somebody who is respected in the community and it's not somebody who just decides to get the title one day.*

An Elder is a specific type of person who holds certain qualities and maintains a certain lifestyle and knowledge base.

> *You have to be completely dedicated to serving the people bringing healing, bringing comfort, bringing consolation, bringing counseling and assistance of other types as well. Elders aren't just focusing on just spiritual matters but could be looking on practical solutions to issues that exist in Indigenous communities... [They are] dedicated to helping Indigenous people, but as well have an inclusive rather than exclusive view.*

Overall, three general distinctions can be made in regards to the definition of Elders:

1. Community Elder
2. Elder/Healer
3. Elder/Teacher

The division of Elders into three specific categories is not an Indigenous practice, and is used here as conceptual framework for the purpose of clarification; nevertheless, these categories may generally be considered valid.

COMMUNITY ELDER

The first category "Community Elder" reflects age and extensive life experience. In this case Elders are male or female Indigenous individuals that have lived a long life and presently maintain a healthy life-style and possess a wealth of practical knowledge. This knowledge may or may not be related to spiritual things and usually involves expertise based on experience.

This type of Elder is often consulted, especially in communities, for assistance in drawing on local cultural practices and knowledge about a variety of topics like traditional diet, traditional hunting patterns and traditional child-rearing practices. This category of Elder, however, is generally *not* the sort associated with healing or institutional work.

ELDER AS HEALER AND ELDER AS TEACHER

The second and third categories are closely related and difficult to clearly differentiate. It is these two classes of Elders that this manual refers to under the single title, Elder. Most cultural advisors consulted also refer to these two types of Elders interchangeably and generally do not included local community Elders in their discussions of specialized sacred roles.

The Elder/Healer and Elder/Teacher categories of Elder are closely related to the role and identity of the traditional healer. Some healers may not be Elders, while all Elders can be considered Healers to some degree. These second and third categories differ in the degree to which traditional healing practices are used. The second category, Elder/Healer, can be seen as focusing on traditional healing specialties while the other category, Elder/Teacher, focuses on cultural teaching and counseling. Indigenous advisors almost unanimously agree on the common essential elements to both of these categories: it is equally as valid to say that Elders are defined as Elders by their common qualities, and that they are differentiated by their individual specializations or skills.

An Elder/Healer may primarily work as a healer who specifically practices traditional medicine in the form of ceremony and/or in the use of Indigenous pharmacology: "there are Elders that are medicine men/women. Also, such an individual might serve as a spiritual leader, a cultural teacher and an exemplary community figure." In contrast, an Elder/Teacher may be an individual who is primarily a cultural, spiritual teacher and mentor who is also an exemplary community figure, a spiritual leader, and yet only minimally practices as a traditional healer: "Elders are not necessarily medicinal people."

The distinction between Elder/Healer and Elder/Teacher is important to make since traditional healers often hold positions of high respect in Indigenous communities, and yet may *not* be considered Elders. As in Western medicine, a person's medical skill and knowledge are not intrinsically reflective of their temperament, capacity for compassion or degree of commitment. Similarly, there are traditional healers who may have the capacity and skill to practice traditional medicine and yet do not exemplify the holistic leadership, compassion and community devotion expected from an Elder. Advisors comment that an Elder is "not going to try and judge you and say 'you can't' or put you down." An Elder is described as "trusting," "accepting," "gentle," "kind," they "love people" and "radiate that love." In terms of healthy spiritually based life styles, "they teach it, and talk it, and live it."

GENERAL QUALITIES OF AN ELDER

Essential in both the traditional healer type and teacher type, an Elder is an Indigenous person who makes a life commitment to the health and holistic healing of their community, Indigenous people, and often all sentient beings - *including* what Western minds would identify as the spiritless physical world.

> *Elders are people who are interested in the well-being of everybody.*
>
> *It's not a personal thing when they are involved helping people. They have that kind of interest of people's well-being and heart... They look at things [and see that] if you are doing well in your life it's going to affect mine and I'm going to have a better life. If your children are happier, my children are happier. If your grandchildren are going to live happy and well, it's going to affect my grandchildren - even if we don't live next door to each other.*

The selfless and lifelong commitment of an Elder emerges from their understanding of their role as a "mediator" of healing and not the source. An Elder's work is based on the understanding that "you have to put [healing] in the hands of the Creator, because that is where the healing is going to come from." An Elder notes, "I am only the worker."

> *A real Elder will never look at themselves as being a healer. They look at themselves as being an instrument... if they have a gift for healing; they will not say it's theirs. It's given to them to help others.*

Because an Elder's understanding of her/his role is based on spiritual experience and a profound sense of calling, and not a career or income-driven choice, issues such as time commitment, life commitment and income, are distinct (see Part III for more on this).

> You do it for the rest of your life...You're not supposed to retire from helping people. You're supposed to do it for the rest of your life.

> We don't generally look at [being an Elder] like a profession the way the public does now. You would look at it as something that they were given to help people.

Healing and leadership may take many forms such as ceremonial conduct, spiritual counseling, social welfare work, or political advocacy. The Elder is a person who selflessly devotes his/her life to the betterment of others. The Elder possesses extensive knowledge of her/his own and likely many other Indigenous traditions; further, the Elder exhibits her/his wisdom in as many aspects of her/his life as possible. The holistic perspectives of Elders are exemplified in their approach to healing. To an Elder "all aspects are important in a person's health: spiritual health, mental health, [emotional health], physical health." Some Elders described the holistic nature of their work.

> Healing isn't just sewing up your cut and keeping it sterile so that it heals. Healing is looking after or helping the person to look after all his or her needs.
> When you really care about a human being it doesn't stop at one segment of their life... when you get involved with people, you get involved in every area of their lives. We don't just help people with their [illness]. We get involved in just about every area of their lives.

GENDER AND AGE

An Elder (Elder/Healer, Elder/Teacher) may be male or female and may be of any age. One Elder commented, "The Spirit recognizes both men and women equally." While it is most common for Elders to be post-menopausal it is acknowledged that some individuals are spiritually gifted, demonstrate exceptional ability and begin to serve their communities at a very young age.

One Elder added that while a young Elder or healer might be difficult for a person in need of care to hold in high regard because of their age, it is never appropriate to assume that a young Elder is not well respected. Even a child, recognized to be a future healer and leader, may be involved in a person's care because of their healing abilities.

> *There are people who are much younger who fit that category [of Elder] or have the gift of helping others and they have an extreme caring for others - more than normal.*

> *It's not just people over a certain age. There are some young people who are just born into that role and who are nurtured from a very young age.*

While most Elders and Cultural Teachers acknowledge that there are exceptions to the expected older age of Elders, some maintain that age is a dominant factor.

> *A traditional Elder is somebody who knows the teachings, is [qualified] to share traditional teachings with you, and they are a certain age. They're older.*

> *An Elder to me is also somebody who is over 55... 60 years old.*

[Age is not essential] but [an Elder's skill] really becomes obvious when they get older.

In general, young Elders are often referred to as 'healers,' 'traditional teachers,' or some other specific term until they reach a more advanced age. One cultural advisor noted that few young healers would accept the title Elder until they had reached an advanced age and/or had been named an Elder by their community.

Though young healers and traditional teachers are not traditionally called Elders and though few would intentionally accept the title, many institutions make the mistake of addressing individuals based on job title. A healer hired to fill the role of an "Elder" is likely a sensible choice. However, that individual should not be referred to as an Elder simply because of the job they were hired to do. Often the "Elder" hired by an institution is in fact a cultural advisor or healer. Such discrepancies are significant to Indigenous people.

In essence, the age and definition of an Elder are closely related to cumulative wisdom and experience. One Elder eloquently addressed this:

An Elder comes into their own particularly when he/she has mastered certain stages of life. Balance can be reached easier when the younger stages of life are behind. Then 'today' can be concentrated on. The 'now' is an important factor in the helping profession: 'being in the now.'

CHRISTIAN INDIGENOUS ELDERS

Even in Indigenous communities where Christianity has all but replaced traditional religious belief and practice, the acknowledgment and utilization of Elders is maintained. In a parallel manner, older, Christian Indigenous individuals that demonstrate sound judgment, a wealth of life-experience, wisdom, spiritual integrity and religious commitment are recognized as Elders. These individuals often fill the same roles as traditional Elders, providing counseling, advice, prayer, and healing rites. In some communities where both traditional Indigenous religion and Christianity are practiced little difference is believed to exist between Christian and traditional Elders.

While the majority of Elders working in health care settings will be traditional in orientation it is important for health care professionals to be aware of Christian Indigenous Elders. It is improper to assume that an Indigenous Elder will never be Christian in belief and practice; similarly, it is not appropriate to assume that all Indigenous families will accept the care and authority of a Christian minister, chaplain or Christian Elder.

THE ELDER'S COMMUNITY

This manual generally refers to "community" in the sense of a closely settled group of people, such as a reservation or rural town. Usually, when speaking of "an Elder's community" the reference is made to their home community or the localized group of people he or she most consistently serves. These two communities may not be the same for a given Elder.

Additionally, it is critical to note that different Elders serve different notions of community, and all are equally valid. Some Elders serve only their home community, some Elders serve a region like the Canadian prairies, and others may choose to work only in certain agencies like hospitals or correctional facilities. An Elder may exclusively work on, local, regional, national or international levels. Some Elders work only with Indigenous people and others work cross-culturally.

An Elder's commitment is closely tied to their gifts, personality and the opportunities that have been presented to them in life. Most cultural advisors and

Elders affirm that different Elders are called upon to serve the world in different ways and that all types of work are necessary.

> *"The community defines the Elder, not the other way around."*

To define who Elders are and what they do is a paradox. Few Elders would call themselves Elders, and some communities do not even define or overtly determine who their Elders are. For many Indigenous communities, the word Elder does not even exist in their language; the role is collectively understood and unspoken: one Elder remarked, "In the community I grew up in it wasn't said, it was just known."

When working with Elders it is important to remember that many of them may be too modest to admit to being Elders. Also, as mentioned, some of the Indigenous spiritual leaders or traditional healers who become involved with health care agencies may be referred to as Elders inaccurately by non-Indigenous staff. The misapplication of the term is common and should not necessarily be a reason to doubt the authenticity of an Indigenous cultural teacher, healer or ceremonial leader. Although, there are many individuals today who seek the prestige and attention afforded to Elders and selfishly claim the title to satisfy personal motives, Elders are best judged by their communities and other Elders.

Regardless of the accuracy of the use of the term Elder, non-Indigenous staff should be supportive and always be open and understanding to the unique contributions and needs of any individual working in the role of "Elder." To be culturally accurate, healers and cultural advisors should be appropriately titled and addressed - and *not* referred to as Elders. Like the differing specializations and titles in Western medicine, this distinction is critical. Despite these important differences in specializations, the majority of the information in this manual about Elders can also be applied to employment and relationships with healers and cultural advisors.

STANDARDIZATION OF PRACTICE

It is difficult to discuss the variety of roles and vocations found in Indigenous communities since few vocations related to healing and spirituality are viewed as "jobs" or as careers consciously chosen. Indigenous Elders, healers and spiritual leaders are generally designated by a number of factors such as family tradition, personal aptitude, a sense of calling, and the influence of the Spirit World.

DIVERSITY OF INDIGENOUS ELDERS, HEALERS, TEACHERS AND SPIRITUAL LEADERS

For most Indigenous Elders and healers, an intimate and real experience of Spiritual Forces and Spirit Beings, such as those of ancestors and sacred animals, plays a central role in their selection and education as specific spiritual leaders. Unlike in Western communities, personal desire and perceived ability are far less significant factors in the development of an Elder or healer. While the Elder remains a culturally idealized role and a holistic embodiment of tradition, there are many other roles and specialized spiritual and healing oriented vocations in Indigenous communities.

Healers, much like Western medical practitioners, specialize in different forms of healing and the treatment of certain categories of illness/disease. A healer may have spiritually been "given" a certain ceremony or herbal medicine which may have a variety of applications. Other healers may specialize in a type of treatment approach, such as one ritually based or one pharmacologically based, and so on. Finally, healers most commonly develop a repertoire or class of illness that they treat; these classes might be as specific as musculo-skeletal, gastrointestinal, neurological, or psychological. "There's all different kinds of healers and all different kind of healers use their own specialized unique way." Another Elder adds,

They are all healers... but they do different things...There is a broad spectrum... I have seen a lot of Indigenous people who are gifted in so many ways and there are so many types [of healers] and people need to understand that.

Do all Elders Use the Same Teachings?

There are a variety of treatment styles, combinations and processes used by Elders. Not only are there different types of healers, and roles of spiritual leadership, but within each category each practitioner will maintain unique and personally distinct practices. Elders are not necessarily homogenous in their approaches.

There is not only one way of smoking a [Sacred] Pipe. There is different ways. There is not one way of running a Sweat Lodge.

There is not just one approach [to healing].

Elders' approaches to life and the healing of individuals and community will be shaped by their cultural tradition, their local variations and traditions, their family tradition, the teachings and practices of their teachers, their own personality and their unique relationship with the Spirit World. This was repeatedly affirmed by the comments of the Elders and cultural teachers interviewed.

There are different tribal variations of a certain ceremony.

Different tribes have different medicines for the same thing.

There are differences within our own culture as well.

One Elder may strictly counsel and pray with patients in a hospital; another may choose to use traditional medicines or smudges (a form of herbal incense/medicine) like Sweet Grass and Sage. It should be understood that variation is both accepted and expected among Elders.

Do Elders Share the Same Philosophy?

While individuality must be acknowledged, most Elders and cultural advisors assert that there are also areas of commonality and consistency among Elders, "there are differences [in our approaches], yes; but the philosophy is the same." "There is not just one approach but I think in general, though, we work the same way."

Some of the most central of these commonalties among Elders are: the life commitment to service and healing, the practice of a psychosocially healthy and spiritually based lifestyle, their perception of self as an "instrument" and not source of healing; and the understanding that spirituality is foundational to all health. Elders and cultural teachers have also indicated that most Elders embrace a philosophy of pluralism: accepting all cultures and races as equal in importance and capacity to contribute to the human community.

In terms of healing, there is a shared acknowledgment of patient-centered holistic care: always addressing mental, emotional, spiritual and physical aspects of a person in treatment. Elders generally recognize that there are emotional or spiritual roots related to most physical and psychological illnesses that need to be treated concurrently. Overall Elders vary greatly in practice and ritual detail. Their philosophies, however, which are highlighted throughout this manual, are generally consistent.

EDUCATION, TRAINING, CERTIFICATION AND CREDENTIALS

The presence of variation among Elders and their approaches commonly leads to questions about credentials. Elders do not belong to any large ordaining or accrediting body. While some Indigenous cultures did and still do have religious societies which internally evaluate, educate and recognize spiritual degrees, such as the Midewewin societies of the Anishinnaabe (Ojibway), some Indigenous communities did not or no longer have such organizations. This, however, does not mean that there is, or was, no formal education of Elders.

> *In a way we're trained formally, but not as institutionalized as [medically related] training.*

> *There is so much education, so much learning. We're just constantly learning; every time we spend time with our teachers we're learning... A long time ago [the students were chosen to study with Elders], we sat and they talked and talked and talked, and we listened and listened and listened.*

> *Or else they would just put you out there [in nature] and you learned by sitting out there, by listening to the world around you, by watching the movement of the skies, the trees and everything.*

> *One of my teachers grew up with his grandmother and he has been learning ever since he can remember.*

The training and education of an Elder, or one who becomes an Elder, is often rigorous, demanding and life long.

> *They don't give you a piece of paper and say, 'Here, you graduated.' It's a life time thing... it's a lifetime schooling from the day you're born until the day you die.*

> *You never stop learning...there's no such thing as retirement.*

Elders are individuals that have spent the majority of their life actively demonstrating the lifestyle befitting an Elder, and participating in ceremonial activity; "there's no such thing as credentials but, I guess, it's how much we do in the ceremonies and how much we learn from there." A central form of training involved studying closely with usually one mentor but occasionally with as many as three or more.

> *You walk with someone else, someone who is already an Elder and you walk with him [or her] for many years before you're recognized yourself as an Elder...*

> *They teach you the many things you need to know about Indigenous spirituality... if you're going into the medicines, it takes a long time for you to recognize those different plants and to be taught the proper way. Even though there is no university as such, there are people out there that are doing that.*

One cultural teacher described the training of Elders in some detail, as well as their own experience of learning about traditional medicine. The process which contains details too lengthy and too private to be recounted here is extremely in-depth and broad. For example, a person may spend years learning about one particular herbal medicine - where it's picked, what it's called in different places, how it's used in a wide variety of circumstances, how it is prepared and how to relate to it spiritually, with respect - before being allowed to administer it for the first time.

Another example of the depth of the training most Elders experience can be seen in the intense demand for each individual to pursue and achieve health in their own life, mentally, spiritually, and physically before becoming involved in the counseling of others.

Each Elder is expected to engage in a devoted pursuit of personal healing. In this way Elders personally understand and have experienced their own healing approaches and they are ensured good judgment which they can impart to those whom they care for.

Ultimately an Elder's credentials lie in their personal history of work and their personal qualities. "Elders have their own manners of education or certification... that is: the test of living and what they have done with their life is their certification... it's given to them by the people, not just one school of training." Compassion and devotion to service are two of the hallmark qualities of a well-respected Elder.

> *Success is measured by whether you are a good person or not. That is more a measure of success in our way of thinking than the little letters at the end of your name... The way a person cares for people is the highest credentials you can have in our eyes.*

(See "The Hiring Process" subsection in Part III for more on evaluating the qualities and certification of an Elder).

HOW DO ELDERS VIEW THE WESTERN EMPHASIS ON ACADEMIC TRAINING AND CERTIFICATION?

Elders generally respect and acknowledge the Western system of education and certification in health care professions; however, they do not view it as superior to Indigenous approaches. In contrast to the Western emphasis on accredited training and the seemingly exclusive acceptance of the validity of Western practices of medicine and health care, some Elders are given to question the apparent brevity and academic emphasis of Western education.

Most Elders begin their education of cultural and healing approaches during adolescence. In contrast to the on-going, life-long experiential education of Elders which often begins at the time of birth, Western certification which may occur after lasting "only eight years or less," is sometimes questioned by Elders. Elders view the qualifications of a person in terms of practical, demonstrated ability and not based on the prestige or number of university degrees acquired.

> *How do Elders view [Western] training*
> *and credentials? It's not important to us...*
> *It would be more important to me to know*
> *that you were a caring man [or woman].*

The overall quality of a person is seen as paramount. Being a "good person," demonstrated through practice and community approval and opinion, is valued above all else.

Cultural Protocol

When asked about issues of protocol and appropriate ways to speak to Indigenous Elders, there is little variation in the responses of Elders and cultural teachers. Simple answers are given and common requests are made.

What Should Non-Indigenous Professionals Know about Working with Elders?

An understanding of culturally appropriate ways of showing respect, non-verbal communication, sharing gifts, use of tobacco, and other cultural protocols are critical for non-Indigenous professionals to know when working with Elders.

RESPECT

Naturally, Elders should be treated with all the appropriate respect and assumption of ability and skill that any professional is accorded. There is no reason to treat an Elder with any less respect or interdisciplinary courtesy than a person would show a nurse, a surgeon, an internist, a psychologist or an occupational therapist. Elders are highly qualified individuals, usually with decades of experience often both within and outside of institutional settings. A person who is an Elder has earned tremendous respect and appreciation in the communities that he/she has served and should be treated as such.

Social and institutionally supported discrimination has exposed most Elders and traditional health practitioners to consistent direct and indirect experiences of discrimination: distrust, disrespect, suspicion and even verbal insult. Years of experience of racism has led many Elders to request the most fundamental levels of respect.

> *Try treating [an Elder] like a human being…; try to stay away from patronizing them because it is not conducive to collaboration.*

Elders and cultural teachers recount seemingly endless stories of their efforts to assist Indigenous patients in coping with experiences of discrimination in institutional care, as well as stories of their own mistreatment as care providers in health care agencies. An experience of openness and respect will be positive and well appreciated by an Elder.

Showing respect and openness to Elders institutionally is also very important to clients because a show of respect for an Elder is perceived as an appreciation of Indigenous culture and community in general. An Indigenous patient or family that observes a sincere rapport between non-Indigenous health care staff and a visiting or staff Elder will feel affirmed and comforted in their care.

Finally, it is important to show respect to Elders and openness to their distinct and possibly very foreign practices since in most cases the Elder is making a sacrifice by working in an institutional setting. Elders become involved in institutional care for the betterment of Indigenous people and rarely for personal gain.

FIRST IMPRESSIONS

A hand shake denoting respect is always appropriate upon greeting an Elder. There is no common dress for an Elder and English is a second language for many of them.

> *I have yet to see an Elder coming [into an institution] that's all dressed up... They're usually just ordinary people... the way they're dressed doesn't mean they are any less an Elder, and they might be a very important Elder out there in the community.*

A "poorly" dressed individual, a person with "broken English" or a person with little Western academic education may also be a highly skilled and respected Elder. A number of cultural advisors interviewed noted many stories of Elders who had been treated with contempt by health care staff because of the way they looked or dressed.

> *They were making fun of [that Elder], the nurses in there, I heard remarks because he was dressed shabby.*

Elders should not be judged based on Western indicators of professionalism. Though many Elders make an effort to learn and respect Western protocol and professionalism, many may still practice primarily in their communities and will maintain unique Indigenous customs. Among some of the most misunderstood Indigenous cultural customs, little eye contact, a soft/quiet speaking voice and reserved participation in conversation are common. Often these culturally appropriate practices are perceived by non-

Indigenous professionals as insults or an indication of dishonesty or a lack of capacity to contribute. Yet, these practices, in fact, indicate the opposite in Indigenous communities. Avoiding eye contact and speaking softly are both signs of respect offered to others in conversation.

An Elder's reserved involvement in discussion may be related to personal issues like the fear of being discriminated against or disregarded by Western professionals. More often than not, however, a reserved manner reflects an Elder's tendency to listen to others closely and to carefully consider their own words before speaking. Information is shared with great care and intentionality. In contrast to Western practice, information is not intrinsically a public or professional right, but an earned privilege.

Conflicts of Context

Working in a health care agency is often challenging for an Elder: an Elder may have to travel from out of town to visit a person in a hospital or clinic; or an Elder may be uncomfortable in institutional settings, either due to their own negative institutional experiences like that of residential boarding school, or simply due to their preference for their home community and setting. Many Elders and cultural teachers feel hospitals and clinics are not spiritually healthy places. It is felt that the number of sick people, the number of spiritually skeptical staff and other complicating factors like the inability to use traditional medicines and the prevalence of unhealthy psychosocial issues among patients, visiting family and staff make health care agencies almost impossible for an Elder to effectively work in.

A medical doctor or nurse might find it difficult to deliver proper medical care among a non-English speaking, non-Western culture, in a remote wilderness environment, with few if any supplies, or pharmaceuticals. Analogously, Elders must make tremendous compromises in terms of their own approach when working in Western health care environments.

WAYS TO APPROACH AN ELDER WITH A QUESTION OR REQUEST

It is important to understand the demeanor, offerings and gifts which are appropriate to use when approaching an Elder. Understanding these cultural protocols will improve communication with Elders.

DEMEANOR

The basic way to approach an Elder with a question is with openness, sincerity, and respect. Questions should not be asked aggressively or with obvious skepticism; such attitudes will act as barriers to effective communication.

> *If you talk too much, you're going to turn them off. They need to be able to share and talk... it starts coming out once they feel people are listening to them and once they know [that they are] going to be respected.*

It is also important to know that Elders will often present their answers in an indirect manner. For example, an Elder may recount a story that seems mostly irrelevant to a non-Indigenous health care professional; yet, stories are complex methods of instruction used by Elders. As one cultural advisor said, when a story is shared, "it is up to the individual who hears it to draw from that story what they need."

Sometimes an Elder might not answer a question; if they feel the answer should be kept in confidence or that it might be culturally misunderstood. In such instances it is critical to accept that Elders will share information if it is relevant to interdisciplinary care and otherwise may not. If an Elder is not forth-coming, it is best to assume that they feel they have nothing of relevance to share with Western practitioners; just because an Elder does not contribute to a discussion or assessment does not mean they are acting with malice or competition. The reserved nature of Elders should not be perceived as a professional insult by Western practitioners. Allowing Elders to share information at their own pace will likely elicit future contributions as trust and rapport may be issues at stake.

Tobacco

When approaching an Elder with a specific request or question about cultural tradition it is most common in Indigenous communities to present the Elder with tobacco and sometimes a gift. Though tobacco is perceived mostly as a recreational substance in Western society, it is still used in Indigenous ceremony. When an Elder is presented with tobacco (loose in a pouch, or even in a few cigarettes) it symbolizes recognition of the importance of the request and the potentially spiritual roots of its answer.

Much of the work of Elders is guided by ceremony, prayer and a relationship with the Spirit World. Tobacco is a mitigating force in each of these factors. Understood as a sacred plant, tobacco is a sacramental and ritually used material; its smoke is a bridge to spiritual realities.

> *It's hard for some of the medical people to be taught to bring tobacco because to them it doesn't mean anything... I know they're busy but I think they have to learn that in order for the Elder to give a teaching, it's just protocol... If they are sending people [to see the Elder] they should learn protocol. They wouldn't send a patient to another doctor without a referral or whatever. It's the same sort of thing.*

Regardless of an Elder's cultural background, the gifting of tobacco with a request or question will almost always be received as very respectful and sensitive to Indigenous tradition.

> *An Elder will always respect tobacco, no matter who gives it to them.*

GIFTS

When requests are large or involved, such as for the sharing of spiritual information, or for the performance of a ceremony, the preparation of a traditional medicine, or similar things involving the time and skill of the Elder, a gift should be given. Even if an Elder is receiving compensation from an institution in an honorarium or salary, it is still appropriate to acknowledge the personal expense that an Elder incurs when acting as a liaison with the community or when performing a ceremony.

Many physical resources and the preparation of them, as well as time spent in prayer and/or ceremony will be necessary for an Elder to respond to a request. These expenses are often absorbed by the Elder. Since an Elder's work is based on spiritual commitment, few will ask for compensation. Thus, it is important to value and acknowledge the Elder's work with a gift.

A practical item for the Elder's work or home or even money in an envelope would show cultural respect and would be deeply appreciated. While some people question the gifting of money, it must be recognized that Elder's are rarely paid on par with Western health professionals and incur a wide range of expenses related to their healing work.

In addition to the sorts of living costs most people must pay, such as electric bills and rent, Elders commonly face travel expenses and ceremonial expenses when purchasing materials for a ceremony, feeding people involved with a ceremony or simply to maintain chainsaws and lawn mowers to secure wood for Sweat Lodge ceremonies and to maintain sacred grounds.

ARE PROTOCOLS THE SAME IN ALL INDIGENOUS CULTURES?

Elders appreciate that health professionals recognize that protocols are culturally distinct. Cultural variations and regional consistencies are useful to understand.

Just as there is variation in the teachings and practices of Elders, there are also many variations in cultural protocol between different Indigenous cultures and communities. There are many different customs and teachings about how to properly acknowledge an Elder.

Particularly in central Canada and north central United States, the Great Plains and adjacent regions, the presentation of tobacco, possibly a gift, and an attitude of respect and humility are standard and recognized protocols.

> *Working with a traditional Elder... whenever you are going to go for spiritual advice, spiritual healing, traditional healing, again, you always go with your tobacco and your offering.*

Though cultural practices vary between regions and communities, a health care practitioner that demonstrates an awareness of the forms of protocol discussed herein will be greatly appreciated by most Elders and healers.

PART III.

WORKING TOGETHER:

ISSUES IN INSTITUTIONAL COOPERATION

Issues in
Institutional Cooperation

The third part of this booklet is designed to address some of the difficult challenges involved in cross-cultural administration and cooperative work. Moving towards the improvement of the relationship between health care agencies, professionals and Elders, this section explores the perspectives of experienced Elders and cultural advisors regarding the conflicts and common areas of concern associated with the involvement of Elders in institutions.

While it is the intention of this section to specifically address the relationship between Elders and institutional settings, many of these same issues and understandings are equally valid and applicable when discussing the relationship between Indigenous traditional healers, cultural teachers and spiritual leaders and institutional settings/professionals. This point is critical to stress since the term "Elder," particularly in terms of Western institutions, is commonly used as a general term for many types of Indigenous counselors, advisors, spiritual leaders and healers. Accepting the relevance of the following sections for work with other Indigenous specialists and the generalized use of the term Elder, this section will refer exclusively to the work of Elders for the sake of consistency in terminology.

Time Commitments and
the Definition of Work

Indigenous Elders generally have a distinct understanding of time that is in direct contrast to the views of time held by Western societies. Deeply connected to a traditional Indigenous philosophy and upbringing, most Elders will not relate to time as something that can be reduced to the calendar and clock.

For most Elders time is understood as multivalent and is experienced as such. Based on a cyclical paradigm, Elders relate primarily to natural cycles of time: seasons, sunrise/sunset, moon cycles, the growth of plants, or the movement of animal populations. Similarly, the cause and effect of actions are understood to occur in cycles; history is not only linear, but cyclical in its patterns. Additionally, the intense and constant relationship between Elders and the spiritual world of ancestor spirits and cosmic forces is not seen as bound by linear time. Spiritual inspiration must follow its own course, as nature does. For example, spring does not occur according to a clock. Spring emerges out of the confluence of a range of complex annual and cyclical factors. Analogously, Elders conduct their lives and work according to the demands and changes in human populations, personal experiences and their environment - conventional time plays a secondary role.

CONFLICTING PERCEPTIONS OF TIME

Differing perceptions of time between Elders and Western health care providers is a common and critical area of conflict in cross-cultural work. In essence, Western professionals adjust their therapies and work commitments according to regular time intervals and schedules. In Western practice time is a commodity and work is defined by it.

For the Elder, time is secondary to work. A task - be it ceremony, counseling, or consultation - will be given all the time felt necessary. Because an Elder's life commitments have no time frame or limit, they have relationship to time that is in direct contrast to the Western work paradigm. If a patient needs only fifteen minutes of counseling, or if they need two hours, then they will be given the time the Elder feels is needed - without regard to other schedules. Most Elders will find it unnatural to adjust their practice around a clock. As a consequence, Elders may have difficulties matching schedules in terms of meeting times and "efficiency."

Time itself is used as an aspect of an Elder's therapeutic approach. Sitting quietly with a family that is grieving for an hour would not be seen as a waste, but as an extremely active and engaged therapeutic intervention. In short, Elders use time differently than most Western professionals. In institutional work, time is the fundamental context and framework upon which activities are organized and carried out.

In contrast, Elders see schedules as emerging from a relationship. An Elder may use time as a tool and generally does not experience time as being divided between work day and private time in the evening, or work week and "weekend off." An Elder is always "on the job" and, as such, paces him or herself accordingly. This may mean taking time to rest or visit with people in the middle of a "work day;" it is important for employers to remember that few Elders quit work at the end of the work day, most go on to other responsibilities. Weekends are rarely spent relaxing and vacations are even more unusual.

DEFINING WORK AND THE WORK DAY

Time conflicts often center on the understanding of work. The issues of time and the definition of work are almost synonymous because of the inextricable relationship between time and work in Western institutions. A person "begins" work at a given time, and "finishes" at a certain time; work occurs within that timeframe and extra time spent working warrants extra payment. A higher number of patients seen in a given time will yield a higher rate of financial return.

Most medical fields, particularly many medical specializations, demand on-call work and/or extended time commitments. These rigorous demands are compensated through payment based on time and pay scales that are generally higher than most careers. In contrast, Elders generally base their work on a form of contextual timing, rather than external time. Many Western health care workers and administrators unconsciously define the work of an Elder by contracted time and not by actual work completed. As mentioned, time commitments do not define work commitments: most Elders are always on-call, either formally with institutions or informally for their communities. Elders also work weekends and evenings after designated work hours are over.

> When you care about something, you don't just care about it during these [set] hours, you don't just care about it Monday to Friday...

The Elder's work is often only recognized by institutions as occurring within regular work hours. Ceremonies held for patients on the weekend, medicines gathered or prepared in the evening, prayers offered daily, and other regular essential elements of an Elder's therapeutic approach are not reflected in salary pay or hourly wage. One Elder working with health care agencies noted that working until "midnight... would be quite common" even following a day shift that begins at eight o'clock in the morning. In these cases the Elder continues to work knowing that he/she will not be paid overtime or compensated in any way. A common response to this challenge is that Elders should learn to do less when they are not "on work hours."

> If an Elder is [overworking], are they doing it because they're so committed? A part of being an Elder (as I'm finding the hard way) is that I need to take care of myself. Now, if I am going to over-extend myself, then how wise is that?

The problem is that much of the Elder's "extra" work is directly related to his/her commitments with the health care agency. Most patients make requests for things like ceremony, traditional herbal medicine, family counseling, or prayers, which occur outside the institutional setting and work hours. These additional activities are rarely reflected in an Elder's work hours or pay.

en ...disciplinary work, all the ...
...rviewed for this project affi... ...d it...
...ough there were concerns expressed about t...
...atment of Elders by health care professionals, n...
...the advisors felt that the Elders should work in entire...
...lation of the health care team.

The more communication you have [between disciplines], the better the chance a [patient] has of getting well too, ...getting what they need.

PROFESSIONAL DEVELOPMENT

It is also important to note that Elders, as well as cultural advisors and healers, never see themselves as complete in their education and training. The ongoing participation in ceremony and the cooperative work with other Elders are viewed as important to an Elder's development and maintenance as a skilled practitioner. Just as many doctors and nurses participate in on-going conferences, work shops, in-services and even regular opportunities for education like daily rounds and grand rounds, Elders also require time for professional development.

The work-related events that Elders attend, such as workshops, ceremonies and cultural celebrations, are rarely regarded as relevant to an Elder's work. As a result Elders are often forced to use holiday and weekend time to support and educate themselves psycho-socially and professionally.

> *What I see being a problem is not giving them enough time to go and do their ceremonies; and taking time to build up their strength and healing.*

The lack of recognition on the part of institutional personnel regarding this aspect of an Elder's development often leads to Elders that burnout. Poor understanding and compromise around these issues have lead to a high turn over of Elders in many institutions.

SUMMARY OF TIME AND WORK

In order to overcome the issues around the conflicts in time and work commitments there needs to be a mutual understanding between the institutional setting and the Elder employed. Some situations will involve more compromise than others for those involved. When working with Elders in institutional environments it is possible to observe the common institutional perception that Elders do not manage time well; however, most cultural advisors indicated that Elders have very strict

...terminating the administration becom... ...certain degree of flexibility must be expected a... built into any Elder's position. Open and respect... communication is vital in this regard. Lateness for wo... absence from meetings and the need for days worki... away from the office should not necessarily be viewe... as a reflection of poor conduct or ability. A well-qualifie... Elder will request these exceptions in order to fill oth... duties as an Elder (which likely comes at great person... expense to the Elder). Most experienced El...

and clear concepts of time.

> "*I was taught years ago that Indian time is a lot stricter than this clock here.*"

One cultural teacher explained that Elders follow a "broad spectrum of time." The conflict between Elders and institutions is that each follows a different concept of time.

It is unlikely that an institution will ever employ an Elder who will work solely with one institution; because Elders cannot refuse to treat anyone who requests their help from the community or elsewhere. Thus, it is important for institutional personnel to recognize at least three critical points to improve their relationships with Elders: Elders work long hours, are always working, and require professional development and support.

First, an Elder generally works longer hours than stipulated, both inside and outside of the institution's context. This can be addressed by maintaining pay levels while reducing clinical hours, or by increasing salaries or hours paid to reflect the amount of related work that is conducted outside the hospital setting.

Second, an Elder is always working, for anyone who might be in need. To expect an Elder to sacrifice community requests in order to singularly serve the health care agency is unrealistic and will eventually result in either the Elder leaving the job or the administration becoming intolerant and terminating the Elder's position.

A certain degree of flexibility must be expected and built into any Elder's position. Open and respectful communication is vital in this regard. Lateness for work, absence from meetings and the need for days working away from the office should not necessarily be viewed as a reflection of poor conduct or ability. A well-qualified Elder will request these exceptions in order to fill other duties as an Elder (which likely comes at great personal expense to the Elder). Most experienced Elder's will honor institutional time commitments and strive to be as agreeable as possible, and compromise should not need to be extreme.

Third, Elders require professional support systems and professional education and development like any other practitioner. These things will make an Elder better able to provide consistently high-quality care.

It should be remembered that institutional settings are inherently compromising and challenging for Elders. When Elders request time to travel to other communities, or participate in ceremonies these initiatives should be supported, not regarded as holidays, and encouraged as an important aspect of professional development and health.

> *I don't think [an Elder] would want to be at [the health care facility] every day if they come to work here. That is the struggle I am having today; I would like to work four days here and one day out there [in the community]...I have to spend at least one day out there doing stuff. But it's hard for the hospital to understand.*

Interdisciplinary Teamwork

When asked about the involvement of Elders in interdisciplinary work, all the Elders and cultural teachers interviewed for this project affirmed its importance. Though there were concerns expressed about the poor treatment of Elders by health care professionals, none of the advisors felt that the Elders should work in entire isolation of the health care team.

> *The more communication you have [between disciplines], the better the chance a [patient] has of getting well too, or getting what they need.*

> *Your getting together as a team is important because that person, that individual, that patient, will have a much better chance of staying well too after they leave.*

Since Indigenous approaches to health and healing are based on a holistic model of care, most Elders and cultural teachers view the sharing of knowledge and the cooperative treatment of an individual as important. The perception that Elders cannot or do not want to work with a health care team is generally false.

Each individual may have biases and varying capacities to work well in mixed professional groups, but few Elders would resist teamwork based on cross-cultural or cross-disciplinary grounds. Most problems in teamwork tend to occur because of the disregard for the valid holistic skills of the Elder.

Many Western health care practitioners still do not acknowledge that an Elder fills many roles analogous to priest, psychologist, social worker, family doctor and senior family member. Further, the Elder's contributions in each and any of these areas are commonly regarded as secondary to the scientific approaches of the West.
Mutual respect, a common theme in the interviews, was strongly emphasized as the key to successful interdisciplinary work.

> *[The difficulties of working together] could easily be solved if we just respected each other's ways.*

> *It would work wonderfully I think if people respected each other's expertise, because an Elder has an expertise as well; so if doctors and nurses respected that, and if the Elder respected how they were taught to do things.*

> *I think [team work] is really, really, good... as long as there is mutual respect.*

The general perception among Elders and advisors is that it is most commonly Western professionals, who do not respect Indigenous approaches, and not the reverse, most Elders feel that time and commitment will bring change in this regard.

> *Keep an open mind; you might learn something.*

> *Don't come in here with a closed attitude that this [Elder] is some hick who doesn't have the knowledge and skills you have. They may be specialists in their own right.*

> *I think we are still teaching [heath care staff] to work with Indigenous people as a team... it just takes time for them to get used to us being around.*

PAYMENT

Payment is an area of common conflict since the views of most Elders on payment is in contrast with the view of institutional administrations. Traditionally, in the past and still in many Indigenous communities, Elders devoted their lives to the needs of their community.

> *In our societies hundreds of years ago... a spiritual healer, advisor, medicine person, had a special role in their community. That role was to be there for the people for Ceremonies. That was their role, and so they didn't go out hunting, they didn't go out gathering; they had to make sure they had their medicines and everything. And so, the community looked after them... If you went for help you took whatever they were going to need and that was your offering - and you gave your best.*

The Elder's role has rarely been associated with material production or for-profit work. Nevertheless, traditional communities recognize the sacrifices that their Elders make and in turn looked after all their material needs through gifts including food, property, labor, and, increasingly today, money. Many communities care extremely well for their Elders and try to ensure them a comfortable standard of living.

> *In our communities, the Elders are really looked after well. They are given an honorarium when they do something... They get paid really well... because they know about the teachings and [we know] how valuable they are.*

In this reciprocal process the Elder devotes his or her life to the service of the community by sharing not only their knowledge and ritual skill, but also their home and property. The home of an Elder is often a refuge and shelter in the community. Young children may spend time with an Elder's family to learn about their culture or to be protected from unhealthy home environments. In any case, an Elder will never ask for payment. Whether running ceremonies for days on end without reprieve, counseling an individual through the night, gathering herbal medicines or accepting children into their home for months at a time, an Elder will not ask for compensation.

Elders experience themselves as designated by the Creator, to help people; personal gain is not a motive for assisting others.

> *An Elder is given that gift [of being an Elder] to use to help other people and it's not used for their own gain. It's not used to make themselves well off... It's not for self gratification.*

An Elder acts out of selfless devotion and not the expectation of reward. As a person devoted to helping people out of compassion and spiritual duty alone, it is part of their philosophy that requesting payment is inappropriate. Requesting payment would demonstrate a measure of self-interest and not full spiritual commitment to their work. "Elders will never go to you and say, 'Well you want to talk to me; it'll cost you fifty dollars an hour' or 'I expect a gift from you.'"

Whether it is herbal remedies or the ability to conduct ceremonies or provide teachings, the skills of the Elder are all viewed as medicines. These medicines, despite their common correlates in Western therapies, like pharmacology or psychology, are understood primarily as spiritual gifts and spiritual in origin. As such, material gain and financial value are not associated with their distribution or administration.

> *One of the strongest teachings is that you do not bargain with your medicine. If you go and hire yourself out to work in an institution as a[n Elder, or] medicine person, there can be repercussions from the Spirit World.*

One cultural teacher recounts a story about healers who suffered for selling their medicines, "a group of traditional healers were hired to work in [a] hospital and they all died off one after another." The experience and understanding of physical and psychosocial repercussions for the misuse of spiritual gifts and abilities is very real for most Elders.

> *Never, never bargain with your medicines in terms of money... You've been given a gift and so you do not sell medicines. You do not sell your gift; because you have been given a gift to help people. Now, that wouldn't be a problem if people remember the teaching of the tobacco and the offering.*

> *The [Elder] who I learn from cannot accept a salary... if he gets anything that says 'payment' or 'salary,' he will not accept it... If they give [him] an honorarium, that is different.*

Because their ability to help others is "a gift given by the Creator," most Elders feel obligated to help any person who respectfully requests help. Personal expense is rarely the concern of an Elder. Reflecting on this, an Elder commented, "If they come for nothing, [no payment], you will still do your best for them."

Finally, payment is seen as an important aspect of the healing relationship between Elder and family or patient. Payment by a third party, such as a health care agency is difficult for some Elders to reconcile.

> *It's up to the individual [patient] to [offer tobacco] because they have to have some input in their own wellness too... [It is] the patient who is at the center of all this, [and they are] responsible for getting the tobacco too.*

The patient's capacity to pay an Elder, through gifts, food, labor or whatever means, reflects the patient's empowerment to return what was given in the form of healing. Healing is seen as emerging from a relationship between the Creator, healer, and patient and the commitment of all parties involved.

> *I am speaking about a client-[practitioner] relationship, that they have to have their own tobacco and they have to have their own offering.*

Indigenous healers do not view patients as passive recipients of care, but important participants in a holistic process.

Payment is seen as relative to each individual's capacity to give. Elders do not expect the same amount of payment from each individual or for each type of service/treatment. Patients are taught to give what they can; in whatever form they can, as a sign of their commitment to healing and their appreciation of the Elder's work. Payment is also seen as a means of consolidating the patient's or client's intent, energy and resolve.

> *It's how [much] you value your life - you can give gifts.*

> *You go [to an Elder] and offer them whatever your healing is worth to you.*

TWO MAJOR AREAS OF PAYMENT CONFLICT

In contrast to the salary or hourly wage system of remuneration in Western institutions, Elders rely on the reciprocal support of their community and the fact that they are valued and rewarded by their community to maintain house and home. Providing a salary or hourly wage for an Elder is difficult. Most Elders and cultural teachers acknowledge two main issues regarding payment: discussing payment and standard of pay.

DISCUSSING PAYMENT

The first major issue that an Elder rarely feels comfortable discussing payment. Not accustomed to asking for specific rates and perceiving the discussion as contrary to their life commitment, an Elder will likely say little to any discussion about payment. The common problem emerging out of this is that institutional personnel often assume that little input into conversations about payment implies that the Elder is comfortable with what is being offered. This is often not the case.

Another central aspect of an Elder's reluctance to discuss payment with institution personnel lies in the important role that payment has in the healing process. As stated above, Elders and many cultural advisors expect payment to come from the individual being healed and not a third party, unless family. While some Elders will accept a salary and others will not, most Elders affirm the importance of having a patient make a contribution or payment in some form.

STANDARD OF PAY

The second conflict occurs when payment, in salary or hourly wage, is assigned. Many Elders, cultural teachers and traditional healers strongly feel that the average payment to an Elder is inappropriately low. Some attribute the low pay to the lack of recognition of an Elder's experience, skill and contribution. Many feel that Western pay scales are so strongly associated with university education and institutional experience that Elders are intrinsically excluded from higher income brackets.

The case made for higher pay of Elders is based on the amount of experience and expertise that most Elders have, as well as the holistic nature of their work: that they can and often do fill several different disciplinary roles. Some cultural advisors openly acknowledge their integrating contribution to the healing experience of people; for these people the value of an Elder's work is no less then the value of life.

> *What kind of value do you put on your life?*
> *You are asking for life-giving healing...*

When Elders and cultural teachers commented on the holistic role they play in hospital and health care settings they described a wide range of skills and therapies that they bring to their practice. Among the most common ones mentioned were: language interpretation; cultural mediation regarding things like cultural beliefs and spiritual visions; prayer; one on one and family counseling; community representation and leadership; providing aftercare referrals; providing traditional medicines and ceremonies like the Pipe and Sweet Grass ceremonies;

crisis intervention; running therapeutic groups like Sharing Circles; and the delivery of staff education and cultural workshops. Though many institutions view Elders much as they do chaplains, an Elder generally contributes a greater range of therapeutic skill and culturally related expertise and activity.

In some institutions there are some Indigenous individuals who may fill both the role of chaplain and Elder. In some of these cases individuals are both recognized Christian ministers and traditional Elders. Naturally, their work is possible since the work of an Indigenous Elder naturally encompasses the work of a chaplain. Conversely, however, a non-Indigenous chaplain's work does *not* extend to the scope of work that an Elder performs.

THE BEST WAY TO COMPENSATE ELDERS

There are many opinions from Elders and cultural teachers on the best way to compensate Elders. It is impossible to provide a single answer or generalization in this regard. The extremes are still held: some cultural advisors suggest that because of the influence and dominance of Western society today, Elders should receive payment and self-advocate higher pay just as other professionals do. Since the reciprocal involvement of community is often not possible and since institutions tend to standardize payment in regular increments of time, traditional practices of payment are seen as not possible.

On the other extreme, some advisors still feel that it is inappropriate for Elders to accept a salary or wage at all. These individuals maintain that Elders must be paid per commitment, usually by the patient or family involved, and with the proper respect for the role of cultural protocol, tobacco and gifts.

Usually cultural advisors that hold this opinion feel that a fair compromise between the institutional obligation to compensate and the Elder's inability to be on a payroll would be the regular use of honorariums, or a system based on the use of honorariums. Some Elders accept cash donations, however, that would present obvious taxation problems for most agencies.

Between these two extremes there are many variations of opinions and different Elders have chosen to solve this problem differently.

Solving the Problem of Payment

Some payment problems can be efficiently resolved through consultation. Other payment issues can be resolved through evaluation.

Consult Elders, Cultural Teachers and Liaisons
While Elders will likely not discuss their pay, an Indigenous liaison worker or other Elders or cultural teachers could be consulted in regards to setting an adequate wage. Not only can these individuals assist in the assessment of payment, but such individuals might be able to respectfully engage the prospective Elder in a discussion about possible forms and measures of payment.

Some Elders may accept a salary, some might only work for honorariums, another might best be paid as a consultant, and yet another might only accept a contribution to their community. The increasing dependence on money as the primary means to secure even the basic necessities of water, shelter and heat are forcing many Elders to compromise their traditional practices in an attempt to secure a steady income and lifestyle.

Evaluating an Elder's Contributions
Elders and cultural teachers have suggested that institutions should attempt to match the contribution that an Elder brings with the manner in which they are compensated. In many cases, the suggestion that an Elder should be paid on par with other professionals such as psychologists or psychiatrists is viewed as

unjust by institutional professionals. Yet, in Indigenous communities, an Elder is one of the most skilled, educated and most highly regarded individuals. Part of the conflict lies in the inability of Western institutions to appreciate different modes of education, evaluation and professionalism.

Payment Summary

Payment is a difficult subject in the relationship between Elders and institutions. Payment remains an issue which must be dealt with on an individual case basis and with some respect and appreciation for cultural complexity. The initiative of administration in the appreciation and evaluation of the Elder/s hired, as well as the use of an advisory Indigenous third party to act as liaison and consultant will be vital to successful payment arrangements.

The Hiring Process

The hiring process varies for institutional and community-based work. Advertising, references, and the community search involve culturally distinct procedures. Evaluating an Elder's qualifications and using the advice of cultural advisors contributes towards making a wise selection.

Institution versus Community Based Work

The hiring of Elders is another area of divergent opinion closely related to the conflicts involving payment. For an Elder, there are many issues around making formal commitments to specific and regular times, payment and places of work. Since the work of Elders has traditionally been community based and without regular time, payment styles, or even locations, working at an institution is an extreme challenge for many Elders.

The regular commitment of an Elder to an institution or Western based agency intrinsically limits an Elder's ability to serve and respond to the needs of her/his own community. The spiritually inspired and community driven lifestyle of an Elder is at times forced to become secondary to the needs and demands of an institution or agency which may or may not have any regard for those other factors in an Elder's life. This is a major area of conflict since community involvement and spiritual ceremony are central to the support system of an Elder.

Institutional work is often an isolating experience for an Elder, reducing their access to traditional collegial assistance and community support. Despite the presence of Indigenous clients, institutional settings are clearly different than community settings in many ways.

Though many Elders are choosing to work with health care agencies and institutions they are not doing so without personal sacrifice. Most Elders, traditional healers and spiritual leaders working in health care agencies are doing so because of their desire to assist in addressing the overwhelming needs of Indigenous people. For Elders working in institutions, personal gain and their community and collegial approval is often tenuous.

How Do You Hire an Elder?

In the cases where an institution or agency has designated it as appropriate to hire an Elder, rather than contract or consult, the first question that naturally arises is: how is an Elder hired?

There are a few immediate answers to this question. According to Western practice most positions have to be publicly posted, such as in a local newspaper or public data base. That is one method. Elders may also, be recommended by other institutions, or they may be solicited from communities. Institutional recommendations are generally viewed as unreliable; whereas community support and input are seen as critical. The use and validity of these approaches will be explored in greater detail in the following sections.

ADVERTISING FOR AN ELDER

Although public postings and institutional references are common means of seeking out Elders, these are not reliable or traditionally Indigenous means of identifying and approaching an Elder for help/hire.

Some Elders and cultural teachers have suggested that advertisements, such as those in the newspaper, are "coming from an institution's need" and that Elders or the family of Elders must accept that they will find the postings there.

> *By responding to an ad, at least you have an in-road into there and for someone to say, 'an Elder who responds to an ad is not bona fide'... that's narrow minded... we're living in the twentieth century, these Elders probably have families, they probably have the same expenses as anyone else who lives in this society and they need to take care of those needs somehow.*

Other Elders and cultural teachers have pointed out that an Elder that is committed to their work and the service of community "will not go around advertising themselves" and would not be looking for hired work or the sorts of paid positions found in newspapers.

> *If you advertise for an Elder in the paper, an Elder isn't going to come and apply for the job.*

These cultural advisors would caution institutions about placing public postings. There is an expressed concern that many individuals not suitable to work as Elders may apply because of attraction to the payment. "There are a lot of people wanting to be Elders now because they hear there is money in it." Since Indigenous advisors are often not involved in the hiring process, unqualified Indigenous people, who are capable of posing as Elders, can be hired.

> *We always have people [apply for work as Elders] who have come for negative reasons... [because] there might be some kind of prestige in it or there may be some monetary value to it.*

INSTITUTIONAL REFERENCES

There is also a divergence of opinion in regards to the importance of institutional references. Some advisors have suggested that Elders can and should be evaluated based on similar criteria as other professionals. These approaches emphasize the importance of good references from both Indigenous communities and recommendations from institutional professionals.

In contrast, an equally strong body of advisors maintains that Western criteria are not always suitable for the hiring of Elders since many Western notions of appropriate skills are contrary or irrelevant to the work of an Elder. For example, many Elders will not have a formal curricula vitae or a written record of their work experiences.

Furthermore, Elders and cultural teachers have openly noted how the lack of understanding between Indigenous and non-Indigenous culture makes it very easy for unqualified Elders to attain excellent recommendations from Western professionals. Institutional employers are cautioned to watch for those Elders who, "really talk good, but they don't really live that way [an Elder should]."

> *It's easy to fudge your resume and make it look really good... How would people in [institutions] know who knows their culture?*

COMMUNITY SEARCH

Most cultural advisors and Elders agree that the best method of identifying and soliciting Elders for institutional work would involve directly approaching Indigenous communities and community representatives, through the assistance of other Elders, Indigenous consultants or "an Elder's council" that could make recommendations.

Though this approach is uncharacteristic of institutional hiring processes, being far more labor intensive than usual, Elders and cultural teachers have stressed the necessity of this "word of mouth" process if healthy and skilled Elders are to be identified. The most qualified and sincere Elders are usually not looking for work, but are selflessly involved in one or more communities. All the advisors consulted regarding this question agreed that approaching communities directly or through Indigenous liaison workers was a suitable way to identify and hire Elders.

HOW DO YOU KNOW AN ELDER IS QUALIFIED?

Generally, most Elders and cultural teachers agree that the best way to identify the skill and quality of an Elder is through the opinions and experiences of the Indigenous communities that the Elder has served. Most advisors agreed that it is important to "check in the community." Elders generally have public reputations and are commonly known in many Indigenous communities, "[if] they've never heard of this person before, you would start to wonder, particularly if you go back to where he [or she] comes from." Not only was it advised that people inquire into the past communities where an Elder has worked, but also to inquire in their home community

Some advisors suggested that it is important to learn about an individual's family life and to consider their skills and personality in a very personal way:

> Look at their family... If you can't do a
> good job with your own family, why would

you do a good job somewhere else?

You can check them out by talking to [Indigenous] people and saying, 'Is this someone you would go to yourself? Is this someone I would send my children to? Is this someone I would send my mother to or my brother or sister to?' And you would have a good idea there.

How do I know who is reputable or who's good?...There's a lot of things you look at, but one of the main things you look at is... how he or she has lived their lives and you look at their family, what kind of job have they done with their families.

Formal job experience and professional recommendations were *not* consistently highlighted as indicators of ability and generally were only seen as a complimentary means of assessing an individual's ability.

There was not always a direct correlation between an individual's past mistakes or past personal problems - such as alcoholism or incarceration - and an Elder's quality or skill. What is more important is how they have overcome those problems and for how long have they lived a healthy and spiritually based lifestyle.

Even if they lived a very negative life; if they have turned things around, you look at the way they believe, look at their families is a good way [to evaluate an Elder].

Another way of assessing an Elder's qualifications involves learning about the Elder's cultural education: who is/was their mentor, what ceremonies do they run, how long have they lived a traditionally based lifestyle? These questions must be asked with respect and may best be directed by another Elder or cultural advisor.

One Elder, who assists in the institutional hiring, shared a bit about how they approach interviewing other Elders.

> *[I am] asking questions to the prospective*
> *candidate for work. You know: 'what*
> *ceremonies do you run? Where do you*
> *run them and how long have you been*
> *running? Where are you from? Where did*
> *you get your training or where did you get*
> *to learn about the ceremonies you run?'*
> *And if they are up front, they'll tell me... If*
> *they are honest, I'll get a sense of if they*
> *are appropriate for the job.*

It was generally maintained that there are a wide range of questions that an Elder or cultural teacher might be able to ask another Elder without offence and with great results for determining suitability for work. Theological questions, questions phrased in Indigenous languages and questions regarding ceremonial knowledge were all mentioned as important. Most of these questions, however, would require a great deal of prior cultural knowledge and respect on the part of the interviewer.

HIRING SUMMARY: CULTURAL ADVISORS AND COMMUNITY BASED COOPERATION

> *If your own community doesn't recognize*
> *you then probably you're not for real; and*
> *if you say you belong to no community,*
> *it's very hard to [validate] yourself.*

Regardless of the range of opinion on the hiring of Elders and the various manners in which an Elder's suitability might be assessed, the common emphasis is on the involvement of Indigenous communities and cultural advisors.

It is understood that most qualified Elders will not be looking for work in public or professional avenues and should be approached at the community level.

like what they talked about or did during the visit.

> I chart all the time... I don't really see it
> as a problem. There are certain things I
> don't document... basically I let [the staff]
> know I was there... That is all they need
> to know.

> I think we [Elders] do chart because it is
> policy in [this health care facility]... we
> have to chart when we visit patients... but
> we choose not to put too much in there.

The need to document is generally associated with the work of institutionally employed Elders and not visiting Elders form the community. Community Elders are often "not expected to be documenting anything."

There are many examples of the range of opinions on documentation: one cultural advisor suggested that she/he feels that the amount and nature of the information disclosed about a patient should be up to the patient. In this approach the patient would determine what the staff would know about the Elder's visit and treatment. In contrast, another Elder commented on how she/he, and other Elders they know, attempt to meet the needs of the institutions by documenting extensively, participating in team meetings and writing reports.

Give and Take

The essential first step in resolving this general area of conflict is to have a very clear understanding, between the Elder and the institution, of what is expected and what is possible for each party. Positions and expectations may have to be adjusted to suit a particular Elder if that Elder is a strong and desired candidate. Conversely, many Elders are willing and able to adjust their standard practices to accommodate institutional demands: "I took the time and sincerely tried to learn the culture of the institution."

Permission

One of the most common means Elders use to respect the confidentiality of patients and still share information with health care teams is to simply ask patients and/or families for permission to discuss things first. Though simple, Elders hold relationships of trust in high regard; some strongly state that they would "never discuss anything that you discussed [with a patient], unless you tell them."

Respect and Communication

The clear definition of roles and expectations, as well as the recognition of cultural difference and style is critical to issues around report writing, administrative duties and confidentiality. A clear line of communication will prevent most problems: some Elders are comfortable writing reports, some are comfortable sharing openly, some would rather leave disclosures and information sharing to the patient, and others still would benefit from the assistance of an Indigenous liaison worker to assist in the sharing/documenting of information.

In terms of confidentiality it is helpful to establish a prior understanding based on mutual respect for differing approaches. Institutional professionals may have to realize that they will not always be entitled to information shared between a patient and an Elder. Respect for this dynamic is the best way to encourage future information sharing - authoritative demands will be counter productive. A number of Elders made comments regarding this and said they have felt forced to share information they consider private. Some of these Elders expressed the hope that the heath care team would try "not to demand that [Elders] disclose... Sometimes there is a fear of being expected to disclose everything that they do."

> *It is very important to know these teachings when [health care professionals]*

work with Indigenous people, and I often tell the nurses or the [first year medical] students that I had a couple of them ask me: 'Well, how do I approach an Elder when I want to know something? Or if an Elder is there doctoring someone if I want to ask something." I just tell them, "If you are meant to know, they will tell you. If you're meant not to know, they won't answer you, they will ignore you." It's as simple as that. But a lot of times I said, "Just go there with a good heart and ask if you need to know something. If you are sarcastic they will pick up your vibes and they won't but if you always ask something in a good way you'll get good results.

FINAL REMARKS

The information in this manual cannot be considered the definitive view on Elders and their work in health care agencies. A manual is unable to represent the true diversity among Elder's views. When possible, individuals who expect to work with Indigenous communities and Elders should make an effort to participate in Indigenous cultural events, workshops and ceremony. Experiential learning is paramount in fostering understanding.

Health care professionals who are genuinely seeking to help meet Indigenous health care needs in a way that is effective and meaningful to Indigenous people will find tremendous support in Indigenous circles. One of the greatest gaps in cultural understanding is the simple human fear of taking the first step towards something unfamiliar. An attitude of respect, humility, sincerity and an openness to learn will easily open doors for health professionals working with Indigenous communities.

The teachings and suggestions in this manual, if applied with true intent, can make a critical contribution to the improvement of the working relationships between Elders, healers, and health care professionals and health care agencies. Moreover, these rarely documented teachings about protocol and worldview have been shared to improve all cross-cultural relationships between Indigenous and non-Indigenous people.

It is with the support of many people, many years of experience and many prayers that this manual has been completed. It is our hope that these words may transform actions, building strong relationships and a better future for Indigenous and non-Indigenous communities working together.

Our gratitude goes to you, the reader, for taking the time to listen.

Meegwetch.

Thank You.

Merci.

Part IV.

Further Readings:

Elders, Traditional Healing, Indigenous Health Care, Indigenous Culture

FURTHER READINGS: ELDERS, TRADITIONAL HEALING, INDIGENOUS HEALTH CARE, INDIGENOUS CULTURE

The opinions and approaches presented in this booklet have been derived from interviews with Winnipeg area Elders and cultural teachers. The ideas expressed are further substantiated by the literature which may be investigated by those who seek further information. The following works have contributed to the overall background of this manual and cover a range of areas related to alternative therapies, Indigenous health care and Indigenous approaches to health, healing and worldview.

Arbogast, D. 1995. *Wounded warriors: A time for healing*. Omaha: Little Turtle Publications.

Beck, P., Walters, A., & Francisco, N. 1992. *The sacred: Ways of knowledge, sources of life*. Tsaile, Az: Navajo Community College Press.

Benor, D. 1993. *Healing research*. Munich: Helix Verlag GmbH.

Benson, H. 1996. *Timeless healing: The power and biology of belief*. New York: Simon & Schuster.

Bernard, R. (Ed.) 1998. *Research methods in cultural anthropology*. Walnut Creek, CA: AltaMira.

Berry, J., Poortinga, Y., & Pandey, J. 1997. *The handbook of cross-cultural psychology: Volume 1 theory and method*. Boston: Allyn and Bacon.

Bobb, J., Bobb, M., Lane, P., & Peter, C. 1988. *The sacred tree*. Lethbridge, Alberta: Four Worlds Development Project, The University of Lethbridge.

Braswell, M. & Wong, H. 1994. Perceptions of rehabilitation counselors regarding Native American healing practices. *Journal of Rehabilitation 60* (2), 33-37.

Canadian House of Commons, Standing Committee on Health 1995. *Towards holistic wellness: The Aboriginal peoples (House of Commons Issue No.31)*. Ottawa.

Canadian Medical Association 1994. *Bridging the gap*. Ottawa.

Couture, J. 1996. The role of Native Elders: Emergent issues. In D. Long & O. Dickason (Eds.), *Visions of the Heart: Canadian Aboriginal Issues* (pp. 42-56). Toronto: Hardcourt, Brace and Co.

Cronin, V. 1997. The Native healing circle. *Aboriginal Nurse 12* (1), 10-11.

Cronin, V. 1997. The Native healing circle. *Aboriginal Nurse 12* (2), 14-15.

Dossey, L. 1989. *Recovering the soul*. New York: Bantam Books.

Dossey, L. 1993. *Healing words: The power of prayer and the practice of medicine*. New York: Harper Collins.

Dossey, L. 1997. *Be careful what you pray for you just might get it.* New York: Harper San Francisco.

Duran, E. & Duran, B. 1995. *Native American postcolonial psychology*. New York: State University of New York.

Ellerby, L, & Ellerby, J. 1999. *Understanding the role of traditional healers in the treatment of Aboriginal sex offenders*. Ottawa: Solicitor General Canada.

Fetrow, C. & Avila, J. 1998. *Professional's handbook of complementary & alternative medicines*. Springhouse, PN: Springhouse Corp.

Feuerman, F. & Handel, M.1997. *Alternative medicine resource guide*. Lanham, ML: Scarecrow Press.

Four Worlds Exchange (Eds.) 1990. *Reclaiming health: Who's responsible for what?* Four worlds exchange II (1).

Gregory, D. & Stewart, P. 1987. Nurses and traditional healers: Now is the time to speak. *Canadian Nurse 83* (8), 25-27.

Hammerschlag, C. 1988. *The dancing healers: A doctor's journey of healing with Native Americans*. New York: Harper & Row.

Hodge, F., Fredericks, L., & Rodriguez. 1996. American Indian women's talking circle: A cervical cancer screening and prevention project. *Cancer 78* (7), 1592-7.

Hultkrantz, A. 1992. *Shamanic healing and ritual drama: Health and medicine in native North American religious traditions*. New York: Crossroad.

Jilke, W. 1982. *Indian healing*. Surrey, BC: Hancock House.

Johnson, S. 1994. *The book of elders: The life stories & wisdom of great American Indians.* New York: HarperCollins.

Kalweit, H. 1988. *Dreamtime and innerspace*. Boston: Shambhala.

Kalweit, H. 1992. *Shamans, healers, and medicine men.* Boston: Shambhala.

Kaufert, J. & Kaufert, P. 1998. Ethical issues in community health research: Implications for First Nations and Circumpolar Indigenous people. *International Journal of Circumpolar Health 57* (1).

Kaufert, J., & Koolage, W. 1985. Culture brokerage and advocacy in urban hospitals: The impact of native language interpreters. *Santee Culture Health 3* (2), 3-8.

Kaufert, J., Lavallee, M., Koolage, S., & O'Neil, J. 1996. Culture and informed consent. In J. Oakes and R. Riewe (Eds.), *Issues in the North vol.1.* (pp. 89-93). Edmonton: Canadian Circumpolar Institute.

Kaufert, J. & Putsch, R. 1997. Communication through interpreters in healthcare: Ethical dilemmas arising from differences in class, culture, language, and power. *Journal of Clinical Ethics 8* (1).

Kellough, G. 1980. From colonialism to economic imperialism: The experience of the Canadian Indian. In J. Harp & J. Hofely (Eds.), *Structured inequality in Canada.* (pp. 343-376). Scarborough, ON: Prentice-Hall.

Kimbrough, K. & Drick, C. 1991. Traditional Indian medicine: Spiritual healing for all people. *Journal of Holistic Nursing 9* (1), 15-19.

Kosowski, M., Grams, K., & Wilson, C. 1997. Transforming cultural boundaries into caring connections. *Journal of Nursing Science 2* (1-6), 83-96.

Krippner, S. 1993. Some contributions of native healers to knowledge about the healing process. *International Journal of Psychosomatics 40* (1-4), 96-9.

Long, D. & Fox, T. 1996. Circle of healing: Illness, Healing, and health among Aboriginal people in Canada. In D. Long & O. Dickason (Eds.) *Visions of the heart: Canadian Aboriginal issues* (pp. 239-269). Toronto: Harcourt Brace.

Longclaws, L. 1996. New perspectives on healing. In J. Oakes & R. Riewe (Eds). *Issues in the north: Vol.1.* (pp. 1-5) Edmonton, AB: Circumpolar Institute.

Mehl-Madrona, L. 1997. *Coyote medicine*. New York: Scribner.

Marbella, A., Harris, M., Diehr, S., & Ignace, G. 1998. Use of Native American Healers among Native American patients in an urban Native American health center. *Archives of Family Medicine 7* (2), 182-185

McClure, L, Boulanger, M., Kaufert, J., & Forsyth, S. (Eds.)1992. *First Nations urban health bibliography: A review of the literature and exploration of strategies*. Winnipeg, MB: University of Manitoba.

Murphy, M. 1992. *The future of the body*. Los Angeles: Jeremy P. Tarcher.

O'Meare, S., & West, D. (Eds.). 1996. *From our eyes: Learning from Indigenous peoples*. Toronto: Garamond.

O'Neil, J. 1986. The politics of health in the fourth world: A northern Canadian example. *Human Organization 45*, 119-28.

O'Neil, J. 1988. Referrals to traditional healers: The role of medical interpreters. In D. Young (Ed.). *Health care issues in the Canadian North*, (pp 29-38). Edmonton: Boreal Institute for Northern Studies.

O'Neil, J. 1993. Aboriginal health policy for the next century: A discussion paper for the Royal Commission on Aboriginal people. In *Royal Commission on Aboriginal People. The path to healing report of the national round table on Aboriginal health and social issues*. Ottawa: Royal Commission on Aboriginal Peoples.

Pargament, K. 1997. *The psychology of religion and coping: Theory, research, practice*. NY: Guilford Press.

Powers, W. 1987. Alternatives to Western psychotherapy: The modern day Medicine Man. In: W. Powers, *Beyond the vision*, (pp 126-146). Norman: University of Oklahoma Press.

Purnell, L. & Paulanka, B. 1998. *Transcultural health care: A culturally competent approach.* Philadelphia: F.A.Davis.

Royal Commission on Aboriginal Peoples. 1993. *The path to healing.* Ottawa.

Ross, J. & Ross, J. 1992. Keeping the circle strong: Native health promotion. *Journal of Speech Language Pathology and Audiology 16* (4), 291-302.

Ross, R. 1996. *Return to the teachings.* Toronto: Penguin Books.

Sanchez, T., Plawecki, J., & Plawecki, H. 1996. The delivery of culturally sensitive health care to Native Americans. *Journal of Holistic Nursing 14* (4), 295-307.

Spector, R.1991. *Cultural diversity in health and illness* (3rd ed.). Norwalk, CT: Appelton & Lang.

Spencer, J. & Jacobs, J. 1999. *Complementary alternative medicine: An evidence-based approach.* St.Louis, MS: Mosby.

Solicitor General Canada. 1994. *Understanding the role of healing in Aboriginal communities.*(Aboriginal Peoples Collection, No. APC 10 CA).

Strickland, D. 1996. Practical innovations: Coping with chaos and change. *AORN Journal 64* (5), 804-7.

Upvall, M. 1997. Nursing perspectives of American Indian healing strategies. *Journal of Multicultural Nursing and Health 3* (1), 29-34, 51.

Vogel, V. 1970. *American Indian medicine.* Norman: U of Oklahoma.

Warry, W. 1998. *Unfinished dreams: Community healing and the reality of Aboriginal self-government.* Toronto: University Press.

Waldram, J., Herring, A., & Young, T. 1995. *Aboriginal health in Canada: Historical, cultural and epidemiology perspectives.* Toronto: University Press.

Waldram, J. 1997. *The way of the pipe.* Peterborough, ON: Broadview Press.

Wall, S. & Arden, H. 1990. *Wisdomkeepers: Meetings with Native American spiritual Elders.* Hillsboro, OR: Beyond Words Publishing.

Waxler-Morrison, N., Anderson, J., & Richardson, E. 1990. *Cross-cultural caring: A handbook for health care professionals in Western Canada.* Vancouver: University of British Columbia.

Young, D., Ingram, G., & Swartz, L. 1989. *Cry of the eagle: Encounters with a Cree healer.*

Young, D. (Ed.)1988. *Health care issues in the Canadian north.* Edmonton: Boreal Institute for Northern Studies.

Young, D., Morse, J., & McConnell. 1988. Documenting the practice of a Traditional Healer: Methodological problems and issues. In D. Young (Ed.) *Health care issues in the Canadian North* (pp. 89-94). Edmonton: Boreal Institute for Northern Studies.

Young, T. K. 1994. *The health of Native Americans: Towards a biological epidemiology.*

Guidelines to Authors

Call for Papers

Aboriginal Issues Press welcomes scholarly papers on Aboriginal issues from all fields (eg.traditional knowledge, social, physical and natural sciences, law, education, architecture, management, medicine, nursing, social work, physical education, environment, agriculture, fine arts and others). Authors from all backgrounds and locations are welcome, including: scientists, poets, educators, Elders, Chiefs, students, and government personnel. All papers (ranging from scientific papers to poetry) are reviewed.

Submit papers in Word following the APA Writer's Style Manual 5th Edition. Maximum length is 10 pages, double spaced, 2.5 cm margins, 12 pt font, Times New Roman. Illustrations must be provided in digital format.

Include sources in the text with author and date for paraphrased information (eg. Flett 1937) and add the page number for direct quotations (eg. Boas 1964, 33). For economy of space exclude footnotes or endnotes.

Capitalize Aboriginal Peoples, Native Peoples and First Nations. Convert all English measurements to metric.

Include a 1-sentence biography, a 50 to 75 word abstract, and your return address with your submission. For further information please contact aboriginal_issues_press@ umanitoba.ca

Books

Aboriginal Issues Press also publishes sole-authored books. Scholars interested in submitting a book manuscript for review must provide the following information to <u>aboriginal_issues_press@umanitoba.ca</u>

1. Table of contents;

2. Two sample chapters representative of the writing style;

3. A curriculum vitae of the author(s);

4. Samples of illustrations, photos, graphs, etc. for the publication;

5. A prospectus which includes the purpose, objectives, and how the author(s) acquired the knowledge shared in the manuscript;

6. A description of the audience and market; and

7. An explanation of why you chose *Aboriginal Issues Press* as a possible publisher.